Andrew Brodie Basics

LET'S DO COMPREHENSION

FOR AGES 7-8

with over **100** reward stickers

- Structured comprehension practice
- A range of fiction and non-fiction texts
- Extra tips and brain booster questions

Published 2015 by Bloomsbury Publishing Plc
50 Bedford Square, London, WC1B 3DP

www.bloomsbury.com

Bloomsbury is a registered trade mark of Bloomsbury Publishing Plc

ISBN 978-1-4729-1954-0

First published 2015
© 2015 Andrew Brodie
Cover and inside illustrations of Alice the Alligator and Andrew Brodie © 2015 Nikalas Catlow
Other inside illustrations © 2015 Cathy Hughes

A CIP catalogue for this book is available from the British Library.

10 9 8 7 6 5 4 3 2 1

Printed in China by Leo Paper Products

This book is produced using paper that is made from wood grown in managed, sustainable forests. It is natural, renewable and recyclable. The logging and manufacturing process conform to the environmental regulations of the country of origin.

To see our full range of titles visit www.bloomsbury.com

BLOOMSBURY

Notes for parents

What's in this book

This is the third in the series of Andrew Brodie Basics *Let's Do Comprehension* books. Each book features a clearly structured approach to developing and improving children's understanding of what they read and how they respond to the texts.

The National Curriculum states that good comprehension draws from knowledge of vocabulary and grammar as well as on knowledge of the world. Children develop comprehension skills through high-quality discussion and from reading and discussing a range of stories, poems and non-fiction. Enjoying the practice in this book will help your child to achieve these skills.

How you can help

Make sure your child is ready for their comprehension practice. Help your child to enjoy the stories, poems and other texts. If necessary, read the texts through out loud, discussing them so that your child really understands what the writing means. Talk through the questions and help your child to choose or compose a correct answer. Support them in writing clear, well-structured answers.

The questions

Each passage is followed by two sets of questions: 'Make it snappy!', which are quick-fire questions to begin with, and 'Chew it over', which may be more difficult. Talk through the questions and help your child to choose or compose a correct answer. Support them in writing clear, well-structured answers. Most children will feel confident with answering the 'Make it snappy!' questions and should be encouraged to move on to the more challenging 'Chew it over' section.

The answer section

The answer section at the end of this book can be a useful teaching tool: ask your child to compare their responses to the ones shown. Their answers will not be identical but should include similar information. If your child has made mistakes, help them to learn from them. Remember that sometimes progress will seem very slow but at other times it can be surprisingly rapid.

Most importantly, enjoy the experience of working with your child – you can share the excitement of learning together!

Look out for...

Alice the Alligator, who may give a helpful or humorous comment about the passage.

Useful words

Useful words, which are listed above the passage. Your child may need these words to understand and answer the questions.

Brodie's Brain Boosters, which feature quick extra activities designed to make your child think, using the skills, knowledge and experience they already have. Can your child answer the Brain Boosters using appropriate and interesting vocabulary?

Contents

My school

Useful words

I've never been to school because there are no schools for alligators!

hundred · assemblies · library · computers

playground · shelter · secretary · assistants

favourite

There are five classes in my school and I think there are about one hundred and forty children altogether. Each class has their own classroom but we also have a big hall for PE and assemblies and we have a library with books and computers in.

Our playground is quite big and it has a shelter in where we can go and chat to our friends. The field is big too and there is a climbing frame in the corner of it near to the playground.

Our headteacher is Mrs Bennett and the school secretary is Mrs Milton. As well as Mrs Bennett, there are five other teachers and six teaching assistants. Mrs Bennett and Mr Hammerton teach the Year 5 and Year 6 classes. Mr Hammerton is the only male teacher in the school.

My class has twenty-eight children altogether. Sixteen are boys and twelve are girls. Our teacher is Miss Turner and I think she's the best teacher in the school.

My favourite subject is maths but I like art as well.

Read beautifully sounding out new words.
19/8/16

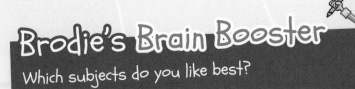

Brodie's Brain Booster
Which subjects do you like best?

Make it snappy!

1 How many classes are in the school?

There are five classes.

2 How many children are there in the school?

There are one hundred and forty children.

3 What is special in the playground?

It is big and has a ~~climbing frame and~~ shelter.*

4 What is special on the school field?

It has a climbing fame in the corner.

* Discussed checking.   19.8.16

Chew it over

5 Write a description of your school.

_____

_____

_____

_____

_____

_____

_____

_____

My house
Useful words

semi-detached   joined   narrow   hallway

downstairs   upstairs   climbing

I live in a swamp, not a house!

My house is a semi-detached house, which means it is joined on to another house. Mr and Mrs Green live in the house that is joined to ours. They don't have any children but they do have a cat called Maurice.

My house has two floors. On the ground floor the first place you arrive at is a porch with narrow double doors – we usually only open one of the doors and it's a bit of a squash getting things in! We keep our shoes and scooters in the porch. When you open the front door you come into a hallway with the stairs in. Next to the hallway is our biggest room, which is a lounge and a dining room all in one. At the back of the hallway is the kitchen, which is just big enough to have a small table where we eat most of our meals.

Upstairs there are three bedrooms and a bathroom. Mum and Dad have the front bedroom. My sister and I have the biggest bedroom, which is at the back of the house near the bathroom. The little bedroom used to be my sister's before she moved in with me. We keep some of our toys and clothes in there.

At the back we have a garden with a lawn and a climbing frame. The climbing frame has two swings, a tower and a slide.

I think my house is the best house in the world and I never want to leave it.

Make it snappy!

1 What type of house is described in the passage?

_____

2 Who lives next door?

_____

3 What is the name of the cat next door?

_____

4 How many bedrooms does the house have?

_____

Chew it over

5 Why can it be difficult to get things into the house?

_____

6 Why do you think the little sister moved into the same room as the writer?

_____

_____

7 Write a short description of your house.

_____

_____

_____

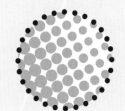

Brodie's Brain Booster
Can you describe your house?

Climbing the tree

Useful words

I've never tried to climb a tree. Alligators aren't very good at climbing!

climbed   difficult   branches   dragged

wooden   steady   easily   tightly

slithered   eventually   fortunately

There's a tree in my garden and I climbed it once. It was quite difficult to get started because there aren't many branches near the bottom. I dragged a wooden garden chair over to the tree so I could reach the very lowest branch. I grabbed the branch then I had to swing my legs over it and pull myself up to sit on it.

After that it was easy to reach the next branches so I could choose which way to go. I stood up on the lowest branch, holding on to the trunk to keep myself steady. I could easily reach quite high up with my hands so that I was able to hold on tightly while I stepped up with my feet.

I kept going higher and higher but the branches were thinner and it started to get a bit windy. I reached out with both hands to grab a small branch but it just snapped and then I started falling.

I slithered down between the branches so that the twigs and leaves smacked against my face as I bounced down from branch to branch. Eventually I dropped the last couple of metres, past the bottom branch and on to the ground.

Fortunately, the garden chair was still exactly where I left it so I was able to start climbing the tree all over again!

Make it snappy!

1 Where is the tree?

_____

2 Why was it difficult to start climbing the tree?

_____

3 What did the writer take over to the tree?

_____

4 What is the higher part of the tree like?

_____

Chew it over

5 Why did the writer fall from the tree?

_____

_____

_____

6 Do you think the writer was injured?

_____

_____

Brodie's Brain Booster

What is the most adventurous thing you have ever done?

Helping at home

Useful words

actually   busy   rudeness   littered

offspring   characters   tidy   cheeky

I hope you are not rude like Alex!

Try acting out this short play script. The two characters are a mother and her child, who has an untidy room.

Mum   What are you doing?

Alex   Nothing.

Mum   Ah, good, that means you're not busy.

Alex   Actually, I am quite busy.

Mum   Well, not too busy to tidy your room.

Alex   My room is really tidy.

Mum   How can you say that?

Alex   I just opened my mouth and the words came out.

Mum   No need to be cheeky. I don't like rudeness.

Alex   Well, what do you like?

Mum   I like someone who isn't rude and who would go and tidy away the stuff that is littered all across the floor of their room, like clean clothes and dirty clothes all mixed together.

Alex   I don't know anybody like that.

Mum   Well, that's funny because I don't know anybody who is going to cook meals for their offspring or wash and iron their clothes or even buy them any Christmas presents!

Alex   I think I'll go and tidy my room.

Mum   Good idea!

Make it snappy!

1 Who are the two characters in the play script?

_____

2 What does Mum want Alex to do?

_____

3 What does Mum say she does for Alex?

_____

4 Does the room get tidied in the end?

_____

Chew it over

5 Was Alex busy? Why do you think that?

_____

_____

6 How was Alex rude?

_____

_____

7 What do you think made Alex decide to tidy the room?

_____

_____

Brodie's Brain Booster

How quickly can you tidy your room?

What time is it?

Useful words

middle · eventually · funnily

moodily · cheerily · remember

I don't like being disturbed at night.

Two girls are sharing a room. One of them is asleep.

Abi What time is it?

Bess What?

Abi What time is it?

Bess I don't know. It's the middle of the night and I was asleep.

Abi Sorry. Just check the time for me. The clock's right next to you.

Bess Oh! It's about half past four.

Abi Oh, is that all? That's good. I'll go back to sleep then. Goodnight.

Bess Goodnight!

Abi quickly falls asleep, but Bess stays awake, tossing and turning. Eventually Bess gets to sleep but shortly afterwards the alarm clock begins beeping.

Abi (Cheerily.) Good morning!

Bess (Moodily.) Good morning.

Abi I had a great night's sleep, did you?

Bess No, funnily enough, I didn't really.

Abi Oh, that's a shame! Why was that?

Bess I slept very well until about half past four but then something woke me!

Abi That's funny, I woke up about then too. I wonder what it was that woke us. Do you remember, I asked you what the time was and you said it was about half past four? Isn't that strange, that we should both wake up about then? I wonder what woke us up?

Bess I don't know what woke you up but I know exactly what woke me.

Abi Oh, what was that?

Bess You! (Hitting Abi with a pillow.)

Make it snappy!

1 Who are the two characters in the play script?

_____

2 Why do you think they are in the same bedroom?

_____

3 What did Abi ask Bess?

_____

4 What happened to Bess when Abi fell asleep?

_____

_____

Chew it over

5 Why couldn't Abi check the clock?

_____

_____

6 Why didn't Bess have a good night's sleep?

_____

_____

7 Do we know what woke Abi? Explain your answer.

_____

_____

Brodie's Brain Booster
Have you ever had a sleepover? How many people were in the room?

Months rhyme

Most years have 365 days, but a leap year has 366 days.

Useful words

leap year | except | alone | month

anniversary | holiday | birthday | calendar

1	2	3	4	5	6	7	8
9	10	11	12	13	14	15	16
17	18	19	20	21	22	23	24
25	26	27	28				

These years are leap years: 2016, 2020, 2024, 2028, 2032

Thirty days has September,

April, June and November.

All the rest have thirty-one,

Except for February alone,

Which has twenty-eight days clear

And twenty-nine in each leap year.

Brodie's Brain Booster

Can you think of one word to describe each month?

14

Make it snappy!

1 How many days are there in April?

2 How many days are there in May?

3 How many days will there be in the year 2019?

4 How many days will there be in the year 2020?

Chew it over

5 Which months have thirty days?

6 Which months have thirty-one days?

7 Why is February special?

8 Write about your favourite month of the year.

Limericks

Useful words

rhyme poem line

humourous nonsense

Limericks are short poems that always have five lines.

There was a young lady from France
Whose feet just wanted to dance.
She said, "Just keep still,
You're making me ill!"
But the feet continued to prance!

There was a young dog from Perth
Who loved to dig holes in the earth.
He buried a bone
And Mum's mobile phone,
I don't know how much it was worth!

Brodie's Brain Booster

Can you write your own limerick?

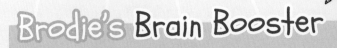

Make it snappy!

1 What country was the young lady from?

_____

2 Which two words in the poem rhyme with Perth?

_____

3 What did the dog like to do?

_____

4 Which town was the dog from?

_____

Chew it over

5 Did the young lady like dancing? Why do you think that?

_____

_____

_____

6 Which of the two poems do you prefer? Can you explain why?

_____

_____

_____

Edward Lear

Edward Lear wrote lots of limericks.

Useful words

twentieth   skilled   illustrations   landscapes

nonsense   talented   published   accomplished

musician   accompany   instruments

Edward Lear was born in a place called Holloway in the year 1812. Holloway is now part of London but in 1812 it was just a village. Edward was the twentieth child in a family of twenty-one children!

As he grew up, Edward became very skilled in drawing and painting. His first book was a book of illustrations of parrots. He travelled to many countries, creating beautiful paintings of the landscapes he saw.

Edward wrote over one hundred limericks, which were published in 1846 in a book called 'A Book of Nonsense'. Twenty-five years later, Edward's most famous nonsense poem was published: it was called 'The Owl and the Pussy-cat'. Another of his poems, 'The Quangle Wangle's Hat', was published in 1877.

As well as being an accomplished artist and writer, Edward Lear was also a talented musician. He could play a variety of musical instruments, such as the guitar and the piano. He wrote music to accompany his poems, including "The Owl and the Pussy-cat".

Make it snappy!

1 In what year was Edward Lear born?

_____

2 What was Edward Lear's first book about?

_____

3 What is the name of Edward Lear's most famous poem?

_____

4 Which musical instruments did Edward Lear play?

_____

Chew it over

5 Why do you think Holloway is no longer a village?

_____

_____

6 What talents did Edward Lear have?

_____

_____

7 In what year was 'The Owl and the Pussy-cat' published?

_____

Brodie's Brain Booster
Do you have a special talent?

On the top of the Crumpetty Tree
The Quangle Wangle sat,
But his face you could not see,
On account of his Beaver Hat.
For his Hat was a hundred and two feet wide,
With ribbons and bibbons on every side
And bells, and buttons, and loops, and lace,
So that nobody ever could see the face
Of the Quangle Wangle Quee.

Brodie's Brain Booster

Which words in this verse do you think were made up by Edward Lear?

Chew it over

Read the description in the first verse of the Quangle Wangle's Hat. Now draw a picture of the Quangle Wangle in the tree wearing his hat.

You will need to read the verse from the Quangle Wangle's Hat very carefully.

Lego

Useful words

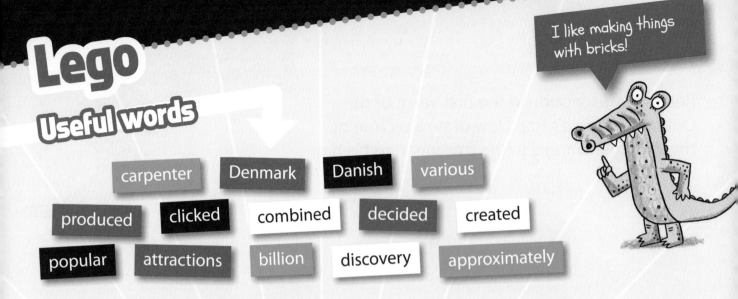

I like making things with bricks!

carpenter | Denmark | Danish | various | produced | clicked | combined | decided | created | popular | attractions | billion | discovery | approximately

Over eighty years ago, a carpenter called Ole Kirk Christiansen began making wooden toys to sell. He lived in Denmark and decided to name his company after the Danish phrase 'leg godt', which means 'play well': he combined the two words to make the name 'Lego'.

Ole Kirk produced lots of different types of toys. In 1949 he began producing plastic bricks, which clicked together and which could be used as building toys. He and his son Godtfred tried making the Lego bricks in various ways, using different types of plastic. After many years they decided that they had created the perfect bricks.

Lego is now one of the most popular toys in the world. Approximately 36 billion Lego bricks are produced every year!

There are seven Legoland theme parks in the world. One is in Denmark, one is in England, two are in the United States of America, one is in Germany, one is in Dubai and one is in Malaysia. There are also eleven Legoland Discovery Centres, which are indoor attractions for families.

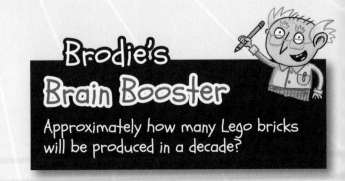

Brodie's Brain Booster

Approximately how many Lego bricks will be produced in a decade?

Make it snappy!

1. In which country was Lego invented?

_____

2. What was the name of the man who invented Lego?

_____

3. What was his job?

_____

4. How many Legoland theme parks are there?

_____

Chew it over

5. What material does a carpenter usually work with?

_____

6. Describe a Lego set you have played with.

_____

_____

_____

_____

_____

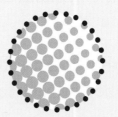

Teeth and eating

My teeth are very important to me and very sharp!

Useful words

nutrition properly swallow healthy

practise incisor canine molar premolar

When human babies are born they have no teeth and they get nutrition only from milk. After a few months their teeth begin to grow but they still cannot chew food properly. At this stage, their parents feed them with soft food that is easy to swallow. The food helps them to grow and to keep healthy. It also gives them the energy to crawl and to practise walking.

Toddlers of about two or three years old have lots of teeth. They have teeth on their upper and lower jaws. They use their front teeth to bite their food. They use their back teeth to chew their food.

As they got older, children lose their baby teeth and their new adult teeth come through. By the time they are teenagers they have thirty-two teeth. There are four types of teeth: incisors, canines, premolars and molars.

The incisors are the sharp teeth at the front of the mouth. Just behind the incisors are the canines, which are usually sharp and pointy. The incisors and canines are used for biting and cutting food.

The premolars are behind the canines and the molars are at the back of the mouth. They are not very sharp but they are wide so that they are very good for chewing food.

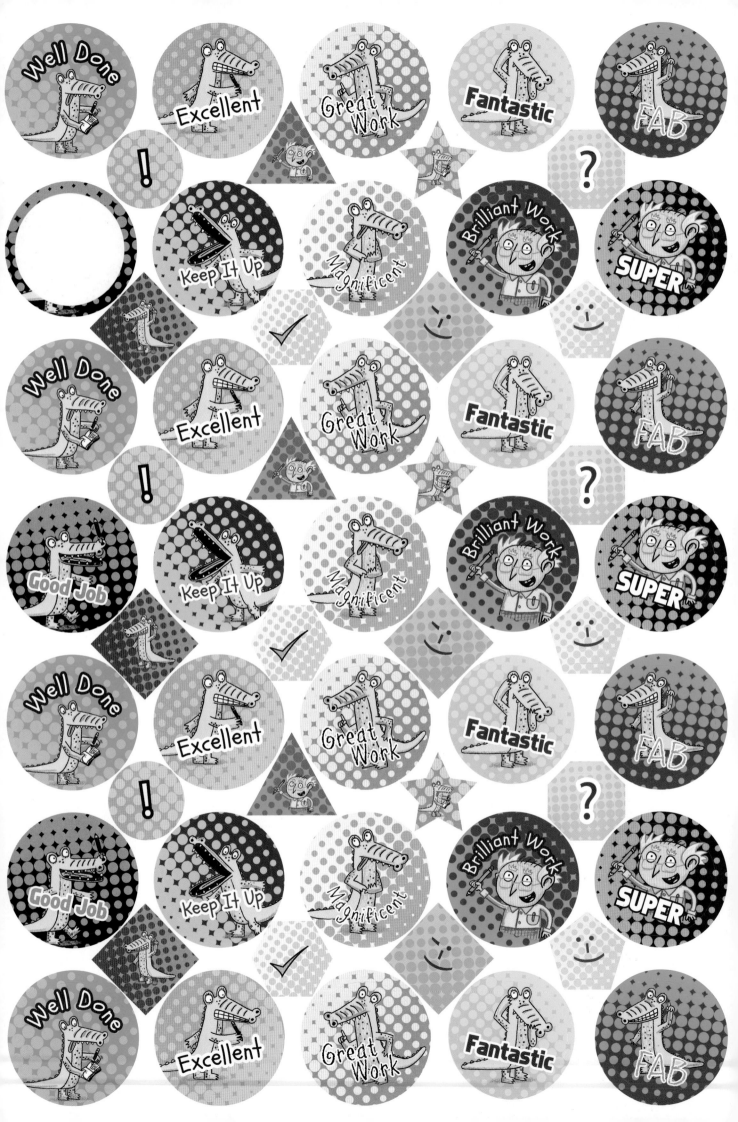

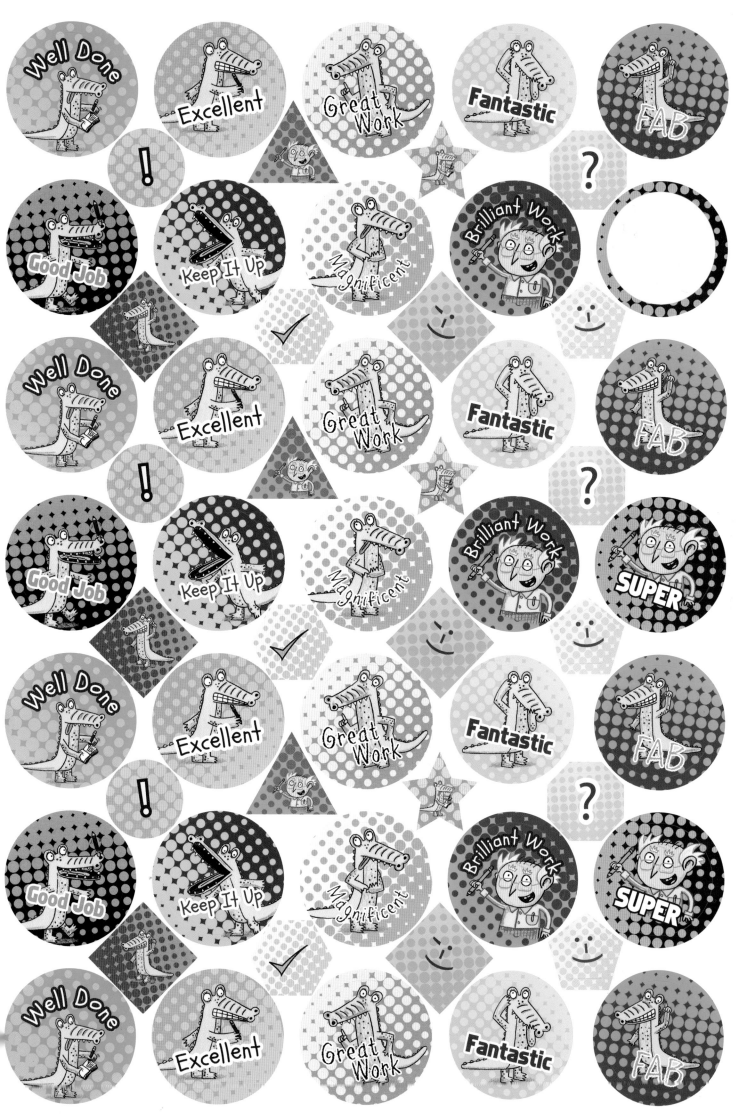

Make it snappy!

1 How do babies get their nutrition?

_____

2 What sort of food do babies have when they are a few months old?

_____

3 How many types of teeth do teenagers and adults have?

_____

4 How many teeth have you got in your upper jaw?

_____

5 How many teeth have you got in your lower jaw?

_____

Chew it over

6 Which teeth are best for biting and cutting food, and why?

_____

7 Which teeth are best for chewing food, and why?

_____

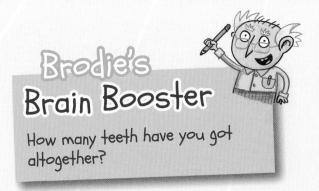

Brodie's
Brain Booster
How many teeth have you got altogether?

Idioms
Useful words

listening   expensive   situation

particular   non-literal   carefully

Idioms are non-literal expressions with particular meanings.

Here are some examples of idioms.

Idiom	Meaning
It's a job to say	I don't know
Give it a shot	Try it
A piece of cake	Easy
Having second thoughts	Changing your mind
I'm all ears	I'm listening very carefully
We're in the same boat	Our situation is the same
Let's call it a day	Let's stop what we're doing
The icing on the cake	The best bit of something that's good
It slipped my mind	I forgot
It's raining cats and dogs	It's raining very hard
It's a rip off	It's too expensive
It costs an arm and a leg	It's very expensive

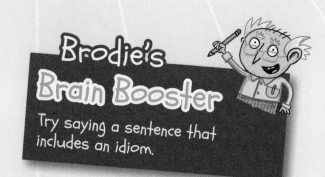

Brodie's Brain Booster
Try saying a sentence that includes an idiom.

Make it snappy!

1 Which idiom means something is easy?

_____

2 What does the idiom 'Let's call it a day' mean?

_____

3 Write a sentence using an idiom that means you forgot something.

_____

_____

4 Write a sentence using an idiom that means it's raining heavily.

_____

_____

Chew it over

5 Which two idioms relate to things costing a lot of money?

_____

_____

6 Write two sentences that include idioms about expensive things.

_____

_____

_____

_____

Idioms involving animals

I definitely don't cry crocodile tears!

Useful words

pretend   exaggerate   clumsily   reveal

Here are some examples of idioms that involve animals.

Idiom	Meaning
Straight from the horse's mouth	From the person who really knows
Putting the cart before the horse	Doing things in the wrong order
A wolf in sheep's clothing	Someone who isn't very nice but pretends to be
Make a mountain out of a molehill	Exaggerate something
Having a whale of a time	Having a really good time
A wild goose chase	A waste of time
A bull in a china shop	Rushing around clumsily
Let the cat out of the bag	Reveal a secret
A fish out of water	A person who is not happy where they are
Has the cat got your tongue?	Why aren't you speaking?
Hold your horses	Stop
Crying crocodile tears	Pretending to be upset

Make it snappy!

1 Which idiom means something is a waste of time?

....

2 What does the idiom 'crying crocodile tears' mean?

....

3 Write a sentence using an animal idiom that means you are really enjoying yourself.

....

4 Write a sentence using an idiom that means someone has given away a secret.

....

....

Chew it over

5 Which three of the idioms involve horses? Write them down.

....

....

....

....

Brodie's Brain Booster

Can you create your own animal idiom?

Alphabet rhyme – part one

Here is the first half of the alphabet.

Useful words

probably gnu includes knit

special knot

It really is a job to say

How many words begin with A.

There may be more or less than B,

Or could there be as few as C?

D has probably got a lot,

I don't know what E has got.

Words with F, there's quite a few,

And G includes the word gnu!

H has horse and hare and hound,

While I has words I haven't found.

Not many words begin with J,

But K is special in a way.

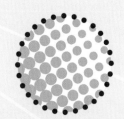

It starts some words like knit and knot,

And makes no sound, like it forgot!

Letter L starts large and little,

And letter M is near the middle.

Brodie's Brain Booster

How many letters are there in the alphabet?

30

Make it snappy!

1 How many letters are mentioned in this part of the alphabet rhyme?

_____

2 What examples are given for letter H?

_____

3 Can you think of more words that begin with H?

_____

_____

4 Where does the letter M fall in the alphabet?

_____

Chew it over

5 What is special about the words **knit** and **knot**?

_____

6 Can you think of other words that start with a silent letter K?

_____

_____

7 Can you think of some words that start with K, where it is not silent?

_____

_____

8 Which idiom appears in the rhyme?

_____

Alphabet rhyme – part two

Useful words

followed   enough   vex

yacht   reached

Here is the second half of the alphabet.

Nice and nest begin with N,

There's out and owl with O, and then

We come to find the letter P

Followed by the Q you see.

Letter R starts roof and rent,

While S starts words like scent and sent!

Would you like a tart for T?

Enough, I hope, for U and me!

V's the start for view and vest,

And W is the start of west.

Do any words begin with X?

It does end words like fox and vex.

And now it's time to just ask Y,

It starts a yacht and ends a fly.

We've reached the final letter, Z,

How many words we must have said!

Make it snappy!

1 How many letters are there altogether in the alphabet?

_____

2 What examples are given for letter N?

_____

3 Can you think of more words that begin with N?

_____

_____

_____

4 Can you think of any words that begin with Z?

_____

_____

Chew it over

5 Can you think of any words beginning with X?

_____

6 Which two letters are closest to the middle of the alphabet?

_____

7 What is special about the words **scent** and **sent**?

_____

_____

Brodie's Brain Booster

Can you say the alphabet backwards?
How quickly can you do it?

Treasure map

Useful words

north   south   east   west

treasure   island   map   compass

It is important to read the questions about the map very carefully.

Here are some examples of idioms.

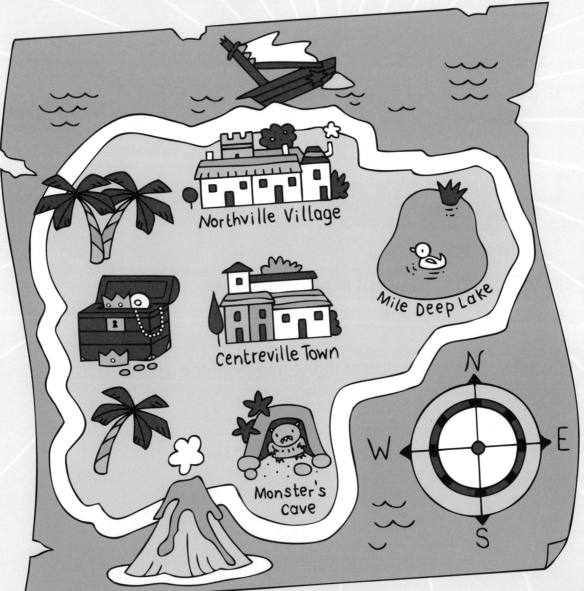

Northville Village

Mile Deep Lake

Centreville Town

Monster's Cave

N
W — E
S

Brodie's Brain Booster

Can you think of a place that is south of where you are now? How about north? West? East? You may need to look on a map.

1 How deep do you think the lake is?

2 What is the village called?

3 What can be found in the south part of the island?

4 What is in the sea north of the island?

Chew it over

5 What is in the sea south of the island?

6 What is due east of the treasure?

7 In which direction would you travel to reach Centreville Town from Monster's Cave?

8 What type of trees are shown on the map?

Coming down to land

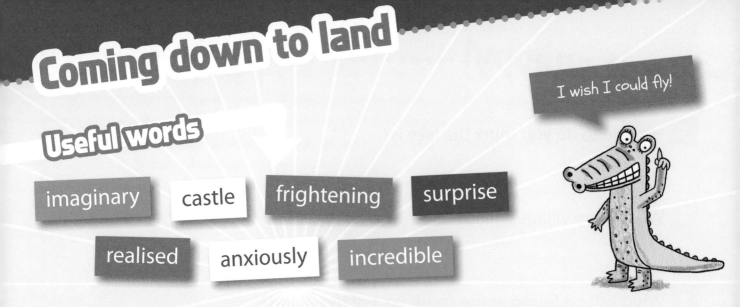

I wish I could fly!

Useful words

imaginary   castle   frightening   surprise

realised   anxiously   incredible

Max gripped tightly to the horse's mane as they flew down towards the castle in the centre of the town. Flying down to land was almost as frightening as when they had taken off. That had been a complete surprise to Max. Horses just don't fly – but this one did!

It had only taken a short time for Max to get used to flying. He had soon found that he loved it! He loved the feeling of the breeze as they flew. He loved the incredible views, looking down on trees, fields and rivers. He loved the thought of telling all his friends about it. They would be so impressed with him!

Looking ahead, between the horse's two ears, the castle seemed to be growing bigger and bigger.

"Are we going to crash?" shouted Max anxiously.

"Of course not!" called the horse. "Don't you trust me?"

"Of course I do!" replied Max. He did trust the horse completely, he realised. He relaxed and enjoyed the landing.

Make it snappy!

1 What is the name of the boy in the story?

_____

2 Where is the castle?

_____

3 How did Max manage to stay on the horse?

_____

4 Why did Max love the thought of telling his friends about his adventure?

_____

Chew it over

5 What was special about the horse?

_____

_____

6 Do you think Max's friends will be impressed when he tells them about the flight on the horse? Why?

_____

_____

_____

_____

Brodie's Brain Booster

It is impossible for horses to fly. Can you think of another story in which impossible things happen?

Arriving at the castle

Have you ever visited a castle?

Useful words

hooves   courtyard   amazing   unusual

slightest   invisible   obvious

The horse's hooves made only the slightest sound as they touched down in front of the castle gates. Max looked round carefully. He was worried that people would be rushing over to see what was happening. There were a couple of people in the courtyard but they were chatting together as if nothing unusual was taking place. There was another horse there too.

"Why aren't they taking any notice of us?" asked Max.

"Because they can't see us, of course!" replied the horse, as if that fact should be obvious to Max.

"You are amazing!" said Max. "You can fly, that's amazing, and you're invisible, which is even more amazing!"

"Yes, I am amazing but so are you!" said the horse.

"Why am I amazing?" asked Max, surprised.

"Don't forget that you're invisible too!"

Max patted his body. He could see it and he could feel it so surely it was visible to everybody. He decided to find out for sure.

Brodie's Brain Booster

Do you think it would be good to be invisible?

Make it snappy!

1 How many people were in the castle courtyard?

_____

2 What else was in the courtyard?

_____

3 Why didn't the people take any notice of Max and the horse?

_____

4 What was amazing about the horse?

_____

_____

Chew it over

5 Why did the horse say that Max was amazing?

_____

6 How did Max check to see if he was invisible?

_____

7 What do you think happened next in the story? Write the next part of the story below.

_____

_____

_____

_____

_____

ANSWERS

The next few pages contain suggestions for answers to the questions in this book. At this stage your child is not expected to answer every question with a full sentence – they can do so if they wish, of course.

The suggested answers highlight the key points that your child should have included. Discuss each of these with them, ensuring that they understand why the given answer makes sense. They may not have written a matching answer but as long as their answer makes sense then that's fine.

Note that the Brodie's Brain Boosters do not need written answers. Your child should be encouraged to talk about their answers, using a range of vocabulary where possible.

My school
Page 4

Brodie's Brain Booster:
Your child needs to answer this question using their own ideas – talk about why they like certain subjects at school.

1. Five
2. We don't know exactly but there are about one hundred and forty.
3. The shelter
4. The climbing frame
5. Your child needs to answer this question using their own ideas. The text will be helpful as your child can follow the structure.

My house
Page 6

1. A semi-detached house, which means it's joined to another house.
2. Mr and Mrs Green and their cat
3. Maurice
4. Three
5. The doors of the porch are narrow
6. Your child can think of their own ideas: perhaps the little sister was frightened to be on her own; perhaps the older child needed company; etc.
7. Your child needs to answer this question using their own ideas. Talk about their house with them.

Brodie's Brain Booster:
Your child needs to answer this question using their own ideas. Talk about your house with them.

Climbing the tree
Page 8

1. In the garden
2. There aren't many branches near the ground.
3. A wooden garden chair
4. The branches are thin.
5. There could be several reasons, indicated by the text: the branches were getting thinner; it was getting windy; maybe a branch snapped.
6. Your child will decide on this but may well consider that there were not many injuries as the writer began to climb the tree again.

Brodie's Brain Booster:
Your child needs to answer this question using their own ideas – you may be able to remind them of something special.

Helping at home
Page 10

Brodie's Brain Booster:
Time your child as he or she tidies a room!

1. Mum and Alex
2. Mum wants Alex to tidy his room.
3. Mum cooks meals for Alex and tidies his room.
4. Yes
5. Your child must decide upon an appropriate answer: it appears that Alex was not busy even though he says otherwise!
6. Alex was cheeky; gave a rude answer to Mum's question 'How can you say that?' – he gave a true answer but not the appropriate one.
7. Mum pointed out everything that she does for Alex.

What time is it?
Page 12

1. Abi and Bess
2. They could be having a sleepover or they could be sisters sharing a room.
3. Abi asked Bess to tell her the time.
4. Bess stayed awake, tossing and turning.
5. The clock was nearer to Bess.
6. Bess couldn't get back to sleep after Abi had woken her up.
7. No, we don't know. She explains to Bess in the morning that she doesn't know what woke her.

Brodie's Brain Booster:
You may need to remind your child about an occasion when they had a sleepover.

Months rhyme
Page 14

Brodie's Brain Booster:
Talk with your child about each month and support their use of vocabulary.

1. Thirty
2. Thirty-one
3. Three hundred and sixty-five
4. Three hundred and sixty-six
5. September, April, June, November
6. January, March, May, July, August, October, December
7. February is special because it usually has only twenty-eight days but it has twenty-nine in a leap year.
8. Your child needs to use their own ideas and explanations.

Limericks
Page 16

Brodie's Brain Booster:
Help your child by searching on the internet or in poetry books and reading a few more limericks together before they write their own.

1. France
2. Earth and worth
3. The dog loved to dig holes.
4. Perth
5. The young lady did not like dancing but she could not stop.
6. Your child has to make their own choice and explanation. You could help by discussing the poems with them.

Edward Lear
Page 18

1. 1812
2. Parrots
3. The Owl and the Pussy-cat
4. The guitar, the piano, and a variety of others (not listed).
5. There are lots more buildings there now; London has got bigger and engulfed Holloway.
6. Edward Lear was an artist, writer and musician.
7. 1871

Brodie's Brain Booster:
Everybody is good at something! Help your child to decide on their best talent.

The Quangle Wangle's Hat
Page 20

Brodie's Brain Booster:

Your child may suggest the following words: Crumpetty, Quangle, Wangle, bibbons, Quee

Your child will need to read and understand the text to be able to draw the picture.

Lego
Page 22

Brodie's Brain Booster:

Approximately 360 billion Lego bricks. You may need to remind your child of how many years are in a decade.

1. Denmark
2. Ole Kirk Christiansen
3. He was a carpenter.
4. Seven
5. Wood
6. Your child needs to write their own description. You could help them by reminding them of Lego they own themselves, or Lego they have used elsewhere. If they have never played with Lego, encourage them to describe another toy or game they like to play.

Teeth and eating
Page 24

1. Babies get their nutrition from milk.
2. Soft food
3. Four
4. Your child needs to count their own teeth.
5. Your child needs to count their own teeth.
6. Incisors and canines, because they are sharp.
7. Molars and premolars, because they are wide.

Brodie's Brain Booster:

Your child needs to count their own teeth.

Idioms
Page 26

Brodie's Brain Booster:

Your child could use an idiom from the list or another one that they know.

1. 'A piece of cake'
2. Let's stop what we're doing.
3. Your child needs to write a sentence including the idiom 'it slipped my mind'.
4. Your child needs to write a sentence including the idiom 'it's raining cats and dogs'.
5. 'It's a rip off' and 'It costs an arm and a leg'
6. Your child needs to write some sentences including the two idioms they have listed in answer to question 5.

Idioms involving animals
Page 28

1. 'A wild goose chase'
2. Pretending to be upset
3. Your child needs to write a sentence including the idiom 'having a whale of a time'.
4. Your child needs to write a sentence including the idiom 'let the cat out of the bag' or 'letting the cat out of the bag'.
5. 'Straight from the horse's mouth', 'Putting the cart before the horse' and 'Hold your horses'
6. Your child needs to write some sentences including the three idioms they have listed in answer to question 5.

Brodie's Brain Booster:
Your child needs to use their own ideas.

Alphabet rhyme – part one
Page 30

Brodie's Brain Booster:
Twenty-six. Your child may know this or they could work it out from the fact that this page shows half of the alphabet (thirteen letters).

1. Thirteen
2. Horse, hare and hound
3. Your child can list any words that begin with H.
4. Near the middle
5. They begin with a 'silent' or 'unsounded' letter K.
6. Your child can list any words that begin with a silent K.
7. Your child can list any words that begin with K, when it is not silent.
8. 'A job to say'

Alphabet rhyme – part two
Page 32

1. Twenty-six
2. Nice and nest
3. Your child can list any words that begin with N.
4. Your child can list any words that begin with Z.
5. Your child may wish to use a dictionary to search for words that begin with X.
6. Letters M and N
7. Scent and sent sound the same but have different meanings (they are homophones).

Brodie's Brain Booster:
Time your child saying the alphabet backwards.

Treasure map
Page 34

Brodie's Brain Booster:
Show your child a map of your area and discuss places that are north, south, west and east of your location.

1. A mile deep
2. Northville Village
3. Monster's Cave
4. A shipwreck
5. A volcano
6. Centreville Town
7. North
8. Palm trees

Coming down to land
Page 36

1. Max
2. In the centre of town
3. He gripped/ held on tightly to the horse's mane.
4. He thinks they would be impressed with him.
5. The horse could fly and talk.
6. They may be but possibly not: they may not believe Max. Has your child used their own ideas to answer the question 'Why'?

Brodie's Brain Booster:

Talk about stories that you have shared with your child. There are lots with imaginary and impossible events.

Arriving at the castle
Page 38

Brodie's Brain Booster:

Your child needs to answer this question using their own ideas. Encourage them to realise that there would be both positive and negative aspects.

1. Two
2. A horse
3. Max and the horse were invisible.
4. The horse can fly and it is invisible – and it can talk!
5. Max is amazing because he is invisible.
6. He patted his body.
7. Your child will need to use their own ideas to extend the story. They should start with considering how Max is going to find out if he is really invisible.